Perfect

THE PLAY

by

Joanna Kenrick

Based on the gr8read novel *Perfect*
by Joanna Kenrick

First published in 2009 in Great Britain by
Barrington Stoke Ltd
18 Walker St, Edinburgh, EH3 7LP

www.barringtonstoke.co.uk

ISBN: 978-1-84299-644-7

Printed in Great Britain by Bell & Bain Ltd

Introduction

In the story *Perfect*, Kate's best friend steals her boyfriend Dan. I'm lucky, as that's never happened to me. But being cheated on is horrible, and I wanted to show how angry and sad it makes Kate.

Turning the story of *Perfect* into a play was harder than I thought it would be. In the book, Kate sometimes says things like "Dan and I went everywhere together", which tells the reader lots in a short sentence. But in a play, you end up having to write a scene to show Kate and Dan having fun. I also had to get rid of the date at the ice rink – how would you do that on stage? I went through the book and chose what I thought were the most important bits. Then I made them into longer scenes, with more talking.

I like the play even more than the book now! I hope you enjoy reading it too.

For Mandie and Dan, with thanks for letting me use his name!

Contents

Cast

Kate

Kate is 15 with light brown hair. She isn't the cool sort – she likes kittens and pink clothes. But she is sweet and kind and will do anything for her friends.

Shannon

Shannon is Kate's best friend and is a lot more street-wise than Kate. She has long blonde hair and perfect nails. She knows what she wants, and most of the time she gets it.

Dan

Dan is 16 and is very popular at school. All the girls fancy him. He likes Kate because she is easy to impress.

Man in cinema

The Man is about forty, wearing jeans and a shirt.

Kate's mum

Kate's mum is easy to talk to. She doesn't want Kate to get hurt by a boyfriend.

Emma

Emma is a girl in Kate's year at school. She loves parties and gossip.

Teacher

The teacher is on duty in the playground and is keeping a look-out for fighting at the gates. (This part only has one line).

Scene 1

Kate's Bedroom

Kate's bedroom is mostly pink and purple. Beside her bed is a small table with a lamp on it. On the floor is a fluffy rug. There is a poster of kittens on the back of the door.

(Kate and Shannon are sitting on the bed.)

Shannon: So what's this all about, then?

Kate: Oh, my God, I don't know how to start!

Shannon: What's happened?

Kate: Only the most amazing thing ever.

Shannon: Go on, you have to tell me.

Kate: Dan asked me out!

Shannon: You are kidding!

Kate: I'm not! I can't think what he sees in me. I mean, I've got big feet and a wonky nose. You, now – you're much better-looking.

Shannon: Well ...

Kate: But he picked me! Shannon, it's like a dream come true.

Shannon: Yeah.

Kate: I mean, I've liked him for so long.

Shannon: Me too.

Kate: That hair ...

Shannon: Those eyes ...

Kate: He's just ...

(Kate and Shannon speak at the same time.)

Kate: Perfect.

Shannon: Perfect.

(Kate and Shannon both sigh.)

Shannon: So when are you going out?

Kate: Tomorrow night. He's taking me
to see a film.

Shannon: You are so lucky.

Kate: I know! Oh, Shannon, you'll
have to help me choose what to
wear.

Shannon: OK.

Kate: I just know we're supposed to be together. Everything's going to be perfect.

Scene 2

The Cinema

Kate and Dan are sitting together. It is dark. There aren't many people in the cinema. A man is sitting a few seats along from Kate and Dan. The film has already been going for an hour.

Kate: Um ... Dan?

Dan: Yeah?

Kate: Are you enjoying this?

Dan: I'm here with you. What's not to enjoy?

Kate:	You're so sweet. I love that we get on so well.
Dan:	You know what they're calling us at school?
Kate:	No, what?
Dan:	Mr and Mrs Perfect.
Kate:	They don't!
Dan:	They do.
Kate:	Aww!
Man:	Shh!

(Kate and Dan watch the film for a bit.)

Dan:	Kate?
Kate:	Yeah?
Dan:	This is a crap film, isn't it?
Kate:	I'm so glad you said that! I thought you were really into it!
Dan:	No way, it's the most boring film I've seen in years.
Man:	Shh!

(Kate and Dan giggle.)

| Kate: | Shall we go? |

Dan: Are you mad? I've paid for these seats!

Kate: You don't want to watch the rest of the film, do you?

Dan: No, I want to watch the rest of the people in here.

Kate: What do you mean?

Man: Will you please stop talking?

Dan: Well, you see that guy?

(Dan points to Man sitting in the same row as them.)

Dan: What do you think of him?

Kate:	What do you mean?
Dan:	He's what – forty? Why's he on his own?
Kate:	Maybe his wife didn't want to come.
Dan:	Maybe he hasn't got a wife.
Kate:	Maybe she left him …
Dan:	… when she found out …
Kate:	… his big secret …
Dan:	… that he likes dressing up in women's clothes!

(Kate and Dan giggle.)

Man: Oh, for goodness' sake! Some

people have no manners!

Man gets up and walks out.

Kate: You're so funny!

Dan: So are you!

Kate: Mr Perfect.

Dan: Mrs Perfect.

(Kate and Dan laugh again.)

Scene 3

Kate's Bedroom

Kate is sitting on her bed, talking to Shannon on the phone. Shannon stands to one side of the stage, lit up by a spotlight.

Kate: And then he told us we had no manners and just walked out!

Shannon: You two! You're crazy!

Kate: I know. It's Dan. He makes me crazy. I'm crazy about him.

Shannon: I wish I had someone to be crazy with.

Kate: You've got me.

Shannon: But I hardly ever see you now. You're always out with Dan.

Kate: Well, why don't you come with us?

Shannon: I couldn't do that. I'd feel like a right gooseberry. Hanging out with Mr and Mrs Perfect.

Kate: Don't be silly. It won't be like that at all. Why don't you come bowling with us?

Shannon: Won't Dan mind? What if he doesn't like me?

Kate: Don't be daft. Trust me, he's going to love you.

Scene 4

The Bowling Alley

Kate, Dan and Shannon are at the bowling alley. Behind them are bowling lanes, with bowling pins set up at the far ends. The alley is loud with the sound of pins crashing, balls rolling, and people talking.

(Shannon is bowling. She takes a big swing at the lane but her aim is bad, and the ball rolls into the gutter.)

Shannon: Oh, God, I've done it again! Right into the gutter!

Dan: You're not having much luck,
             are you?

Shannon: I'm so hopeless!

(It is Kate's turn to bowl. Dan and Shannon are so busy talking to each other that they don't notice her.)

Dan: You're not hopeless.

Shannon: I don't know what I'm doing
             wrong.

Kate: I got a strike!

Dan: I think you're letting go of the
             ball too early.

Kate: You guys, I got a strike!

Dan: Well done, Kate. Look Shannon, it's my turn. I'll show you again.

(Dan picks up a ball.)

Dan: You have to focus on the pins and then follow through, like this. See?

Shannon: A strike! You are amazing!

Dan: It's not that amazing. Go on, your turn again.

(Shannon picks up a ball.)

Shannon: I'm going to miss, I just know it.

Dan: You're not holding it the right way.

Shannon: You do it for me.

Dan: No, you can do it. I'll help.

(Dan stands behind Shannon and puts his hands over hers. Kate doesn't look happy.)

Dan: Now, focus on the pins ... swing back ... let go ... there you are!

Shannon: Eight! Oh my God!

(Shannon jumps up and down and throws her arms around Dan.)

Kate: Well done, Shannon.

Shannon: Did you see? Dan is just the best teacher ever, isn't he?

Kate: Yeah.

Dan: Looks like that's the end of our game. And Kate's won – well done, Kate!

(Dan hugs Kate.)

Shannon: Yeah, well done, Kate. Sorry I was so hopeless. I'll be better next time.

(Shannon looks at her watch.)

Shannon: I've got to go – see you tomorrow!

(Shannon leaves, flicking her hair. Dan watches her go.)

Dan: She's OK really.

Kate: You think?

Dan: Yeah. She's a bit dim, though, isn't she? I mean, it took her so many turns to get it right.

Kate: I know. It's weird. We've been bowling before. She's not normally this bad.

Dan: Maybe my natural charm put her off.

Kate: Yeah, right.

(Kate and Dan laugh. Dan puts his arm around Kate.)

Dan: Hey, don't diss the charm! Do you know how many girls would jump at the chance to go out with me?

Kate: Yeah, you're God's gift, you are.

(Kate punches Dan on the arm as a joke.)

Dan: All right, all right. It's a good thing I've got you to keep my feet on the ground. You keep me sane.

Kate: You're so sweet. Listen – do you mind if next time we go somewhere on our own? Just the two of us, I mean. Not with Shannon.

Dan: I thought you wanted to make sure she wasn't left out.

Kate: I do! But I don't want her with us *all* the time.

Dan: OK. How about I take you out to dinner?

Kate: Where?

Dan: I'll choose the place. Just make sure you wear something posh.

Kate: Posh? Wow – OK, then!

Scene 5

A Restaurant

The restaurant is a classy place. The lights are low. On each table there are flowers and a candle. There is classical music playing.

(Dan and Kate are sitting at a table together. Dan is wearing a tie. Kate is wearing a sparkly necklace.)

Dan: You look amazing.

Kate: I can't get over this place! It's going to cost a fortune!

Dan: I saved up from my weekend job. You're worth it.

Kate: You're the best. Thanks so much. I love being with you.

Dan: Me too.

(Kate and Dan clink their glasses together. At that moment, Shannon walks into the restaurant.)

Dan: Oh, look – it's Shannon.

Shannon: I just came in to say hi! Don't you two look glam!

Kate: How did you know where we'd be?

Shannon: Dan needed a bit of help choosing where to eat, and I said it was nice here.

Dan: So I booked it! And you were right, Shannon. This place is great – Kate was just saying how much she liked it.

(Kate is annoyed that Shannon has shown up.)

Kate: Yeah, I *was*.

Dan: Listen, as you're here, why not join us?

Shannon: Are you sure?

(Shannon pulls up a chair to their table and sits down.)

Shannon: That's so nice of you – Kate, is that OK with you?

Dan: Oh, Kate won't mind. You are her best friend, after all.

Kate: Yeah, yeah, I guess so.

Shannon: Cool! It's so good to see you guys. Wow, look at the lovely food on this menu – how will I ever choose?

(Dan leans over to Shannon to point out something on the menu to her. The lights go out on the stage.)

Scene 6

The Park

It is a warm evening. The sky is just starting to get dark. There is no one else around.

(Dan and Kate are sitting on a bench. They are holding hands.)

Dan: Thanks for this evening. You do like your little secrets, don't you?

Kate: I just wanted you all to myself, that's all.

Dan: Hey, I like that too. It was you who wanted to ask Shannon along in the first place, remember?

Kate: I know. I just didn't think she'd come out with us so much. I never get you to myself, she's always turning up. Like the restaurant last week.

Dan: Is that why you lied to her this afternoon? It was her on the phone, wasn't it?

Kate: Yes. I told her I was staying home tonight. It's my dad's birthday tomorrow so I said my mum and I were baking a cake.

Dan: As if!

Kate: I know, I know. But I didn't want to tell her where I was really going. She'd have wanted to come too.

Dan: Why can't you just say you don't want her around?

Kate: Because then she'd be upset and I'd feel bad. I wish she had a boyfriend too.

Dan: Why hasn't she? She's really pretty.

Kate: You think she's pretty?

Dan: Well, yeah, I guess. She's got nice – hair.

(Kate takes her hand away from Dan's.)

Kate: Can we talk about something else?

Dan: OK, like what?

Kate: I don't know ...

Scene 7

Outside the School Gates

It is the next morning. Through the gates you can see a long, low school building. Students are going in through the school gates, chatting and laughing.

(Shannon is waiting. She has her arms crossed and she is tapping her foot. She looks angry. Kate comes in, carrying her school bag and humming a happy tune.)

Kate: Hi, Shannon, you OK?

Shannon: Why did you lie to me?

Kate: Er ... what do you mean?

Shannon: You said you were staying home. Baking a cake. A *cake!* Was that the best you could think of?

Kate: But I was.

Shannon: No, you bloody were not! I rang your house, Kate. Your mum told me you were out with Dan. Why did you lie to me?

Kate: OK, I'm sorry. It's just – I wanted to have more time with him. You know.

Shannon: What are you talking about? You're always having time with him!

Kate: Yes, but not alone. Not just him and me.

Shannon: Are you saying you don't want me around?

Kate: No! Well, sort of, but ...

Shannon: No, that's fine. Don't say any more. I get it. Three's a crowd, right? And if I'm not around, you can be Mr and Mrs Perfect, can't you? You and your perfect

boyfriend. Well, you know
what? He's not as perfect as
you think. See you around,
Kate.

(Shannon walks off. Kate stares after her.)

Kate: Not as perfect as I think? What
does she mean?

(Dan runs in.)

Dan: Hi, babe. Listen, Pete's having a
party next weekend. You want
to go?

Kate: Uh ...

Dan: It's at this cottage somewhere.
             In the country. No adults
             allowed. It sounds so cool!

Kate: Oh, right.

Dan: We can all stay over, too.

Kate: Stay over?

Dan: Yeah, like a big sleep-over.

(Dan puts his arms around Kate and talks softly in her ear.)

Dan: We could get really close ... keep
             each other warm ... and maybe

... you know ... what do you
think?

Kate: Um ... I'm not sure. Have to ask
            my mum. Call you later?

Dan: Sure, babe.

(Dan kisses Kate. The school bell rings.)

Dan: Gotta run – see you!

*(Kate watches Dan as he goes. She looks
worried.)*

Scene 8

Kate's Bedroom

(Kate is sitting on her bed. She is thinking out loud.)

Kate: "Not as perfect as you think."
What did Shannon mean? Does
she know something about Dan?
Something that I don't? What if
– what if he's been talking to
her about me?

*(There is a knock at the bedroom door.
Kate's mum comes in.)*

Mum: You OK? You seemed a bit down when you came in.

Kate: Mum, how can you tell if a boy likes you? I mean *really* likes you. Not just playing you along or something.

Mum: I'm not sure there's an easy answer to that. Sometimes you can see it in his eyes. But sometimes not. I think you just have to trust your own feelings.

Kate: But what if you're confused?

Mum:	Then the best thing to do is to cool off for a bit. Take a break. Don't see him for a while.
Kate:	He's invited me to a weekend party.
Mum:	Do you want to go?
Kate:	I don't know.
Mum:	Then don't. If you're meant to be together, it'll all work out somehow. Don't feel you have to rush into anything.
Kate:	I just want things to be perfect.

Mum: No such thing, sorry. No one's perfect.

Kate: Dan is.

Mum: Then why are you confused? No, Kate, trust your feelings. If you're not sure you're ready, take it slow. If he really likes you and you really like him, then missing one party won't matter. It's better to be sure.

Kate: Thanks, Mum.

Mum: No problem. Tell him I've said you can't go. That way he won't blame you.

Kate: Good idea.

(Mum turns and leaves the bedroom. Kate reaches for her phone.)

Scene 9

Outside the School Gates

It is **Monday** morning before school.

(Kate is waiting for Dan by the gates. A girl in Kate's year called Emma comes in, talking on her mobile.)

Emma: I know, it was so cool. I'm still tired, are you? I bet Pete had a bad hangover. What a great idea though, to get a cottage. And in the country, too, so we could be as loud as we liked. Best party I've ever been to. Did

I see who? Oh, Dan! Yeah, I
know!

Kate: Er – you're Emma, right?

Emma: He is so lush! Shame I wasn't
the lucky one.

Kate: Can I just ...

Emma: Hang on a moment.

*(Emma stops talking on her mobile and turns
to Kate.)*

Emma: Yeah?

Kate: I – er – Dan told me he wasn't
going to the party.

Emma: You've got to be kidding! He was the party master!

Kate: Oh.

Emma: He said he'd just split up from his girlfriend and he was looking to have a good time. Well, he sure looked like he was having a good time! He spent most of the night snogging the face off that girl.

Kate: Which girl?

Emma: Um ... Sally? Sharon? No – Shannon, that was it. Shannon. She looked pretty happy, too.

(Emma turns her back on Kate and starts to talk on her mobile again.)

Emma: Yeah, I'm still here, sorry. What were you saying about you and Kevin?

(Emma goes in through the gates. Kate stands there, in shock.)

Kate: Dan and Shannon! I can't believe it! God, I'm such an idiot – she must have been planning this all along! All this time, Shannon was just trying to get Dan for herself. I *knew* there was something going on. How could I believe Dan when he said

he liked me? I must have been
blind!

(Shannon comes in. She has her hair in a
new style and is wearing her shirt collar
turned up.)

Shannon: Hi, Kate. You OK?

(Kate walks up to Shannon and punches her
in the face.)

(Dan runs in and stands looking at Shannon
and Kate in shock. Shannon holds her nose,
in pain. A teacher, who has seen everything
from the other side of the gates, rushes out
and shouts at Kate.)

Teacher: Kate Carson! Report to the Head's office right now!

Dan: Kate, what have you done?

Kate: I thought you were the best thing that could ever happen to me. But my mum was right after all. No one's perfect.

(The stage goes dark.)

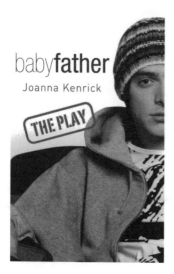

Babyfather: The Play
by
Joanna Kenrick

I'm pregnant!
Micky's girlfriend is
pregnant.
Mickey is 15.
Is there a way out? Or
is Mickey going to be a
dad?

Mind-Set: The Play
by
Joanna Kenrick

Mark and Shaleem are
best mates.
But the bombs change
everything.
Will Mark stand up for
Shaleem when it
matters?

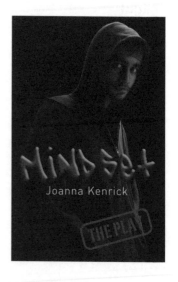

Blade: The Play
by
Chris Powling

Stay away from Toxon. That's what they tell Rich. They tell him about the Blade too, and what it can do to you. But Rich is in the wrong place at the wrong time.

Alligator: The Play
by
Theresa Breslin and
Julie Gormley

Jono has a problem. He's just got himself an alligator. His mum is going to kill him. Unless the alligator gets there first ...

You can order these books directly from our website at
www.barringtonstoke.co.uk